A Kalmus Classic Edition

Sigfrid

KARG-ELERT

THIRTY STUDIES

Opus 107

FOR FLUTE

K 04491

30 STUDIES

FLUTE

SIGFRID KARG-ELERT, Op. 107

3

4

Appassionato e stretto (♩.).(Leidenschaftlich, treibend (rasche ganze Takte.)

6

Rapido e brillante. (Rasch und glänzend.)

9.

8

f con fuoco
(feurig)

Leggero, grazioso e veloce. (Locker, zierlich, geschwind.)

12.

sempre pp
(durchweg pp)

Flatterzunge

Mosso e leggerissimo. (Sehr leichthin, schwebend.)

15.

12

Un poco mosso, umoristico. (Etwas lebhaft, mit Humor.)

16.

Leggero veloce, giocoso. (Leicht, spielend, sehr rasch.)

17.

Adagio (quasi cadenza). (Adagio (im Stile einer Kadenz).)

18.

con fuoco (sehr heftig) — f allargando (breit) vivace (lebhaft)

14

16

*) r ritardando (breit, zurückhaltend)   aa   accelerando assai (sehr drängend)
   a accelerando (rascher, eilend)   r...a...aa... lento da principio, poi stringendo sempre più fino al rapidissimo (langsam beginnend, rascher
                                                                                                    und drängender bis hastig)

Un poco vivace e capriccioso. (Ziemlich bewegt, kapriziös.)

25.

Capriccioso, con civetteria. (Kokett und kapriziös.)

26.

NB. Die Quintolen können anfänglich als ♪♪♪♪♪ (²⁄₅) geübt werden. Später ist auf Ausgleich Gewicht zu legen.

NB. *The quintuplets must at first be practised as* ♪♪♪♪♪ (²⁄₅). *Later they must be equally balanced.*

Un pochettino mosso (ben articolato). (Leise bewegt (deutlich phrasiert).)

27.